WHEN MAGIC REALLY HAPPENS

Join Little Bear in a sparkling and breathtaking adventure
as he discovers the real magic of Christmas,
and meets someone very special on Christmas Eve...

Written by Helen Ford and Louise Holmes

Illustrated by Lizzie Walkley

with Special Thanks to James Gray and Russell Wilson

Visit www.foreverfriends.co.uk
to see the movie 'When Magic Really Happens'

Printed and bound in China.
First edition, September 2009.

When **MAGIC** really happens

When the lights on the Christmas tree

twinkle and glow

And the whole world is hushed by a blanket of snow,

Then every bear knows it's that time of the year

For hugging up closer to those they hold dear.

One Christmas, they gathered
to dream of each thing
They hoped and they wished
that Santa would bring...

Snug by the fireside
they toasted their toesies,
Making roast chestnuts
and warming their noses.

In the glow of the firelight as everyone chattered,
One bear was thinking of what really mattered...
How Santa brought presents at Christmas each year...
But who gave *him* something when Christmas was here?

Santa worked hard and he never forgot,

He came down each chimney, he brought such a lot...

How nice it would be for Santa to find

A gift that said, "Thank you for being so kind!"

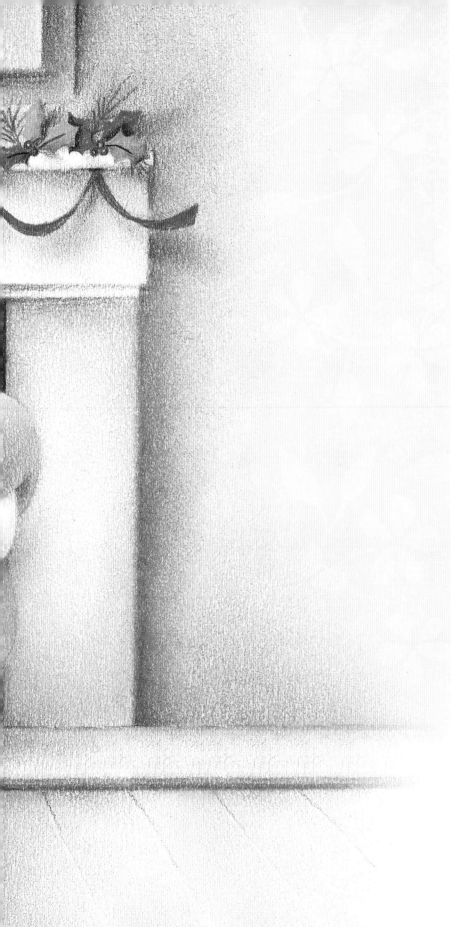

Christmas Eve came
and the stockings were hung,
Mince pies were eaten
and carols were sung,
The tree lights were twinkling,
the candles burned bright
And the stars were all shining
as day turned to night.

Sleepy small bears climbed the stairs to their beds

With pictures of presents filling their heads,

Except for one bear who nervously knew

That this Christmas, he had something special to do.

When he was certain the bears were all sleeping

(He checked every one, to make sure they weren't peeping),

The little bear tiptoed downstairs just to see

How pleased and excited Santa would be.

Then Santa appeared and straightaway saw
The parcel marked 'Santa' that lay on the floor.

He opened it up and his cheeks were aglow

As he cried, "Well! What's this?"

and laughed "Ho! Ho! Ho!"

He looked round the room and he saw Little Bear,

Hiding behind a big comfy chair...

"It's to thank you," said Bear, "For being special, you see.

It's a big cuddly, warm, loving, snug hug from me!"

Santa was beaming,
he held the hug tight —
He said, "I will always
remember this night."

With a smile bright as sunshine
he took the bear's paw,
And just as he did,
the bear's feet left the floor.

In moments, Bear found himself perched in the sleigh,
And Santa was shouting, "Let's go now! Away!"

Then the reindeer took off, to Bear's great surprise,
And their hooves climbed on clouds
as they sailed through the skies.

They flew with a whoosh and a thundering sound,
Looking down to the lights of the town on the ground.
They flew over cities, past buildings and cars,
Bouncing on moonbeams and riding the stars.

They danced on the darkness —
Bear lost sense of time...
One moment they'd dive,
the next they would climb...

Then they landed so softly, so feathery light,
It was hard to believe they'd just flown through the night.

"Thank you," said Bear,
"For a wonderful time."
Santa smiled warmly,
"The pleasure's all mine."

"Goodbye, Little One,"
and he cuddled the bear,
"Now I really must go —
There's no time to spare!"

The reindeer flew Santa back into the sky,
And he huggled the hug as he waved Bear goodbye...

Bear was so pleased
with what he had done —
Thinking of others
was really such fun.

The bears were all wondering where he had been —

And he thought of the wonderful things he had seen...

But what could he tell them? Where would he start?

So he kept his adventure locked safe in his heart.

When the lights
on the Christmas tree
twinkle and glow,
Remember what Bear did —
and then you will know...

That the real Christmas magic,
that lasts all year through,
Comes from giving to those
who are closest to you.

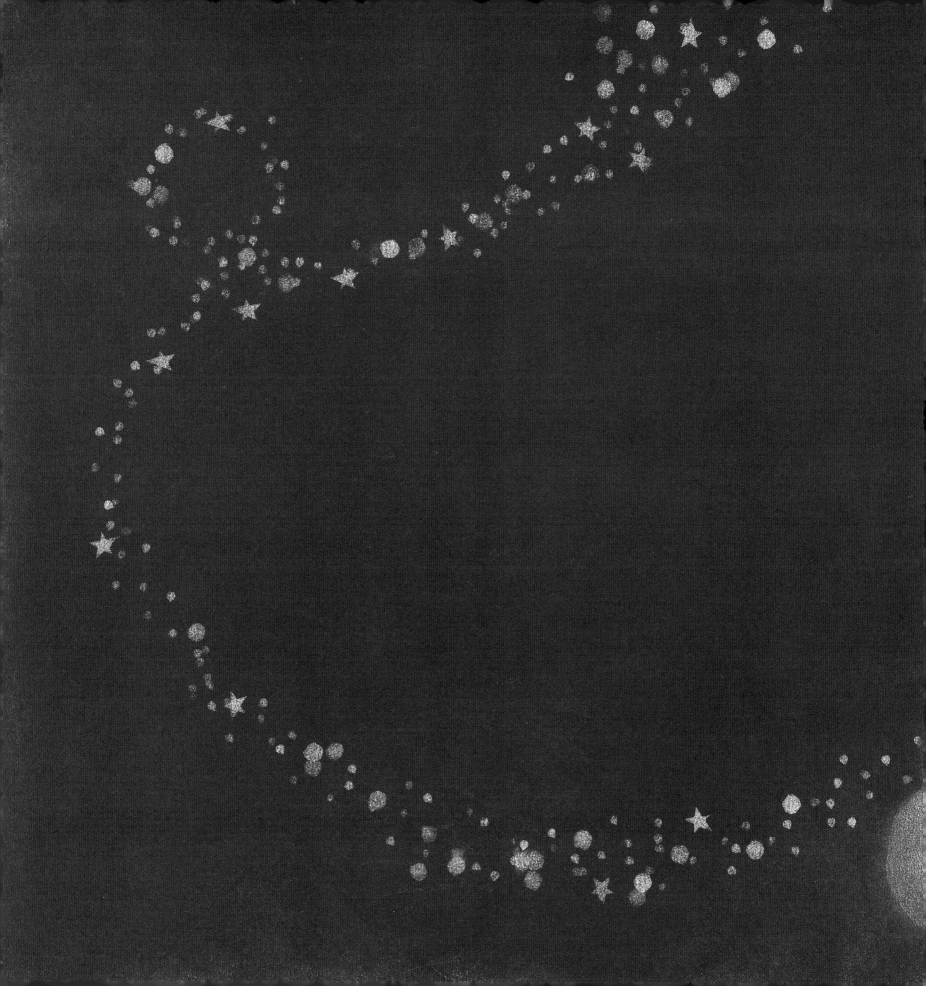